Bond

Assessment Papers

Starter papers in
Non-verbal Reasoning

Alison Primrose

First edition published in 2004 by:
Nelson Thornes Ltd

This edition published in 2007 by:
Nelson Thornes Ltd
Delta Place
27 Bath Road
CHELTENHAM
GL53 7TH
United Kingdom

10 11 / 10 9 8 7 6

A catalogue record for this book is available from the British Library

ISBN 978 0 7487 8104 1

Illustrations by Nigel Kitching
Page make-up by Wearset Ltd

Printed and bound in Egypt by Sahara Printing Company

What is Bond?

This book is part of the Bond Assessment Papers series for non-verbal reasoning, which provides a **thorough and continuous course in non-verbal reasoning** from ages six to twelve. It builds up non-verbal reasoning skills from book to book over the course of the series.

What does this book cover?

Non-verbal reasoning questions can be grouped into four distinct groups: identifying shapes, missing shapes, rotating shapes, coded shapes and logic. This book lays the early foundations through practice of four question types: finding the odd one out, completing a visual sequence, completing a picture story and completing a visual analogy. All the questions at this level involve pictures so that they are similar to the picture puzzles with which children may already be familiar. Later in the series pictures will be replaced by shapes.

The age given on the cover is for guidance only. As the papers are designed to be reasonably challenging for the age group, any one child may naturally find him or herself working above or below the stated age. The important thing is that children are always encouraged by their performance. Working at the right level is the key to this.

What does the book contain?

- **5 papers** – each one contains 24 questions.

- **Scoring devices** – there are scoring boxes at the end of each paper and a Progress Chart at the back. The chart is a visual and motivating way for children to see how they are doing. Encouraging them to colour in the chart as they go along and to try to beat their last score can be highly effective!

- **Next Steps** – advice on what to do after finishing the papers can be found on the inside back cover.

- **Answers** – located in an easily-removed central pull-out section. If you lose your answers, please email cservices@nelsonthornes.com for another copy.

How can you use this book?

One of the great strengths of Bond Assessment Papers is their flexibility. They can be used at home, in school and by tutors to:

- provide regular non-verbal reasoning practice in **bite-sized chunks**
- **highlight strengths and weaknesses** in the core skills
- identify **individual needs**
- set **homework**
- set **timed formal practice** tests – allow about 15 minutes.

It is best to start at the beginning and work through the papers in order.

What does a score mean and how can it be improved?

If children colour in the Progress Chart at the back, this will give an idea of how they are doing. The Next Steps inside the back cover will help you to decide what to do next to help a child progress. We suggest that it is always valuable to go over any wrong answers with children.

Don't forget the website . . . !

Visit www.assessmentpapers.co.uk for lots of advice, information and suggestions on everything to do with Bond, helping children to do their best, and exams.

Paper I

Which is the odd one out? Circle the letter.

Example

a b c d

1 a b c d

2 a b c d

3 a b c d

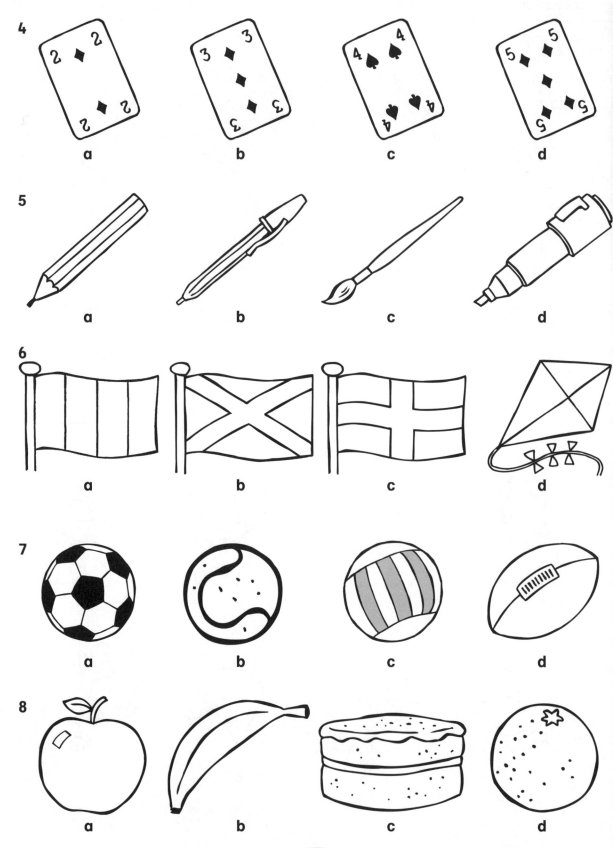

4   a   b   c   d

5   a   b   c   d

6   a   b   c   d

7   a   b   c   d

8   a   b   c   d

Which one comes next? Circle the letter.

Example

a   b   c   d

9

a   b   c   d

10

a   b   c   d

3

11

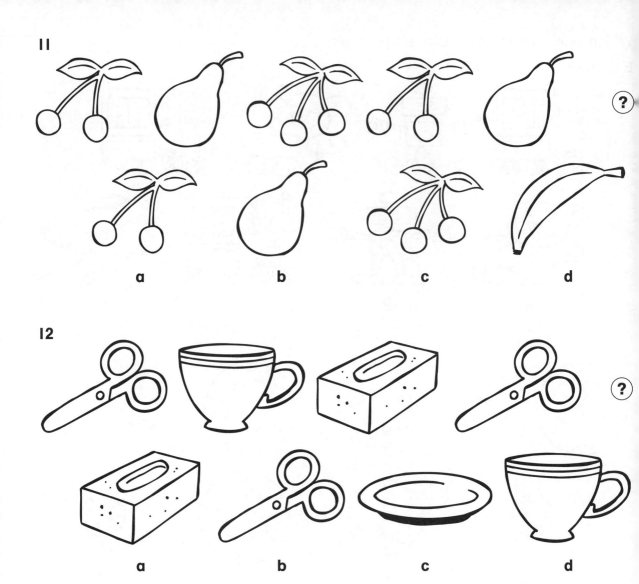

a   b   c   d

12

a   b   c   d

These pictures tell a story. Which one comes next? Circle the letter.

Example

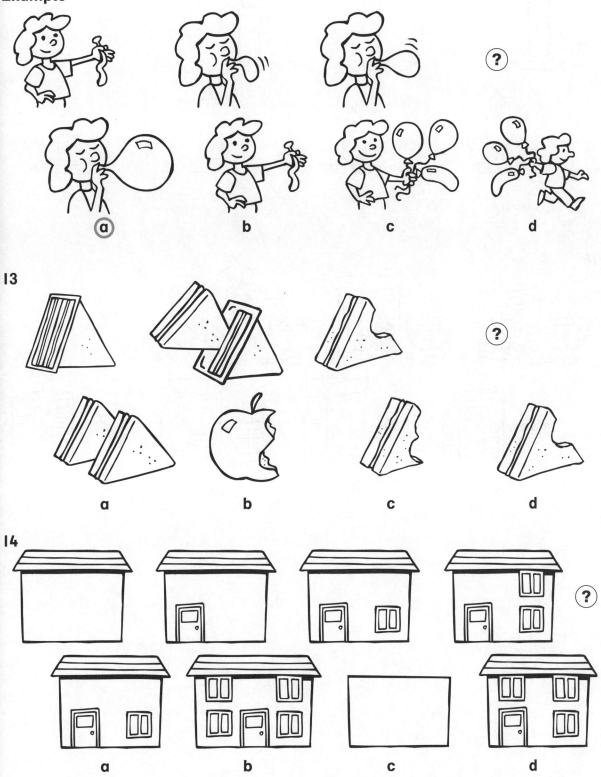

15

16

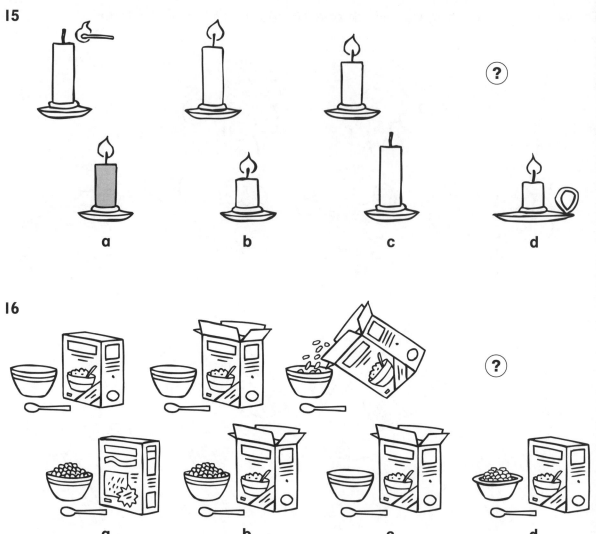

Which picture completes the second pair in the same way as the first pair?
Circle the letter.

Example

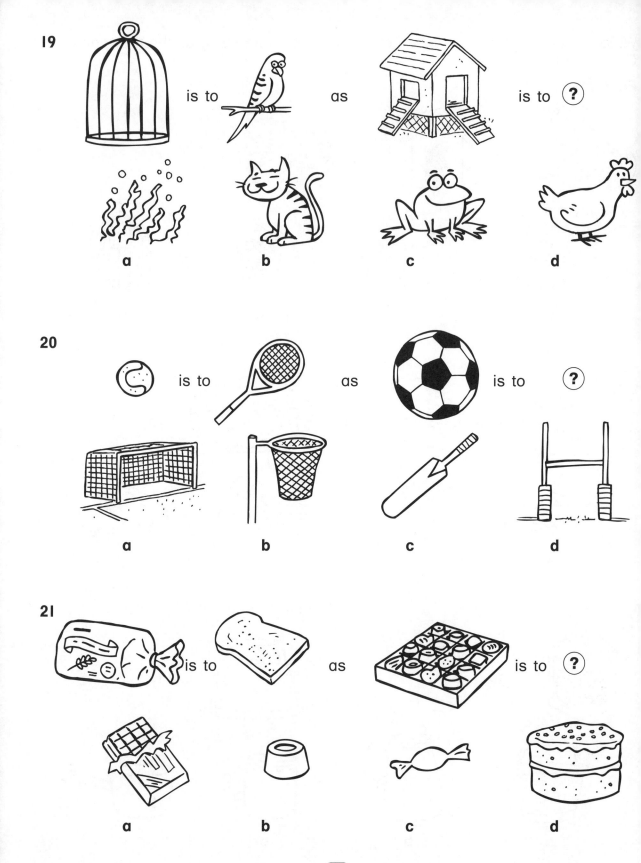

19 is to as is to **?**

a b c d

20 is to as is to **?**

a b c d

21 is to as is to **?**

a b c d

Paper 2

Which one comes next? Circle the letter.

Example

a   b   c   d

1

a   b   c   d

2

a   b   c   d

3

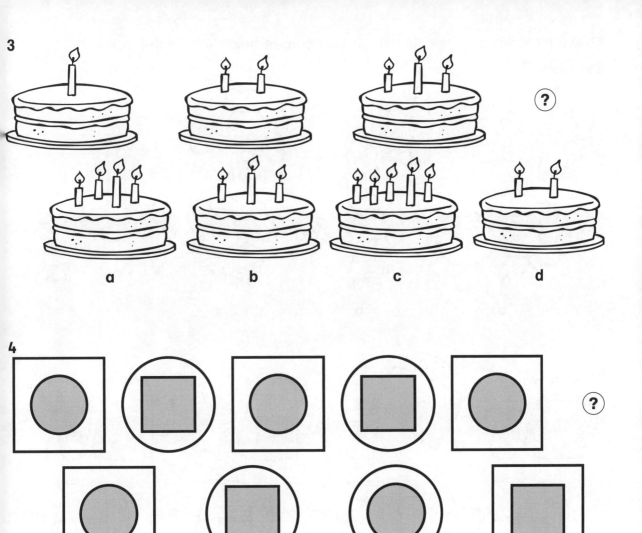

a   b   c   d

4

a   b   c   d

These pictures tell a story. Which one comes next? Circle the letter.

Example

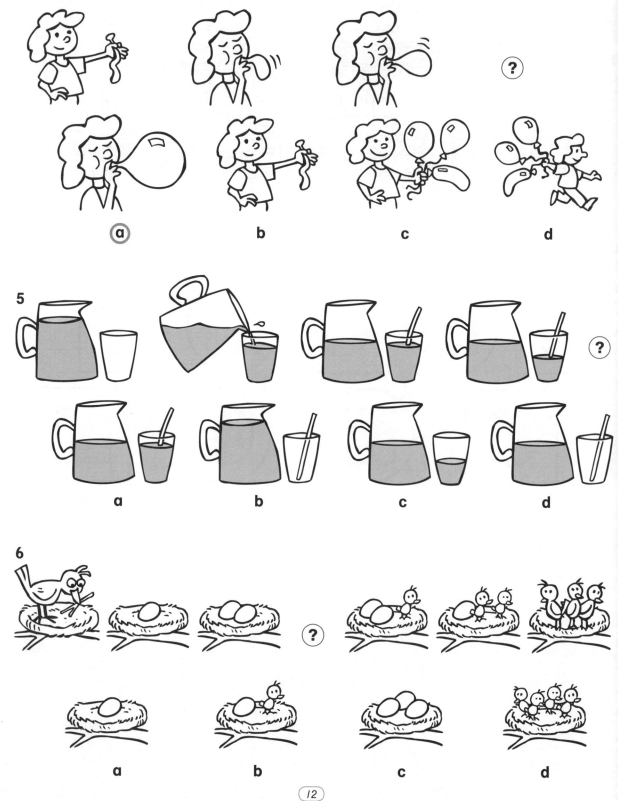

7

a b c d

8

a b c d

Which picture completes the second pair in the same way as the first pair?
Circle the letter.

Example

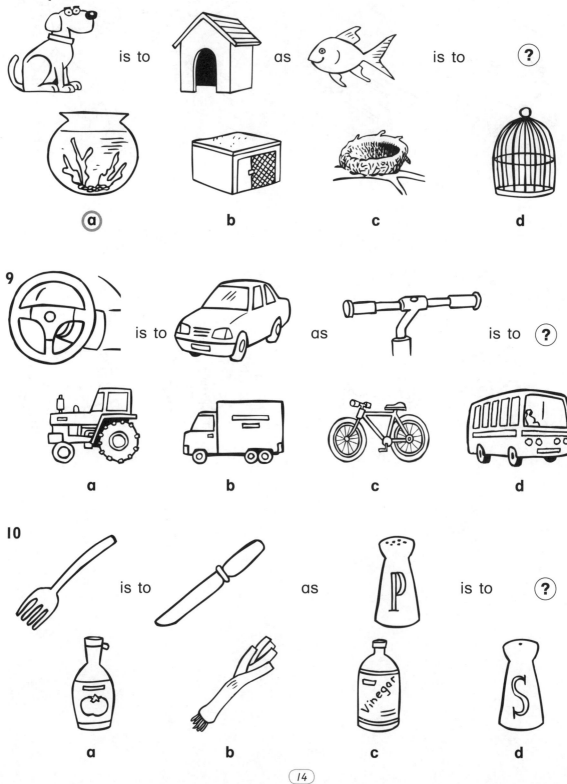

11 is to ___ as ___ is to **?**

a   b   c   d

12 is to ___ as ___ is to **?**

a   b   c   d

13 is to ___ as ___ is to **?**

a   b   c   d

14

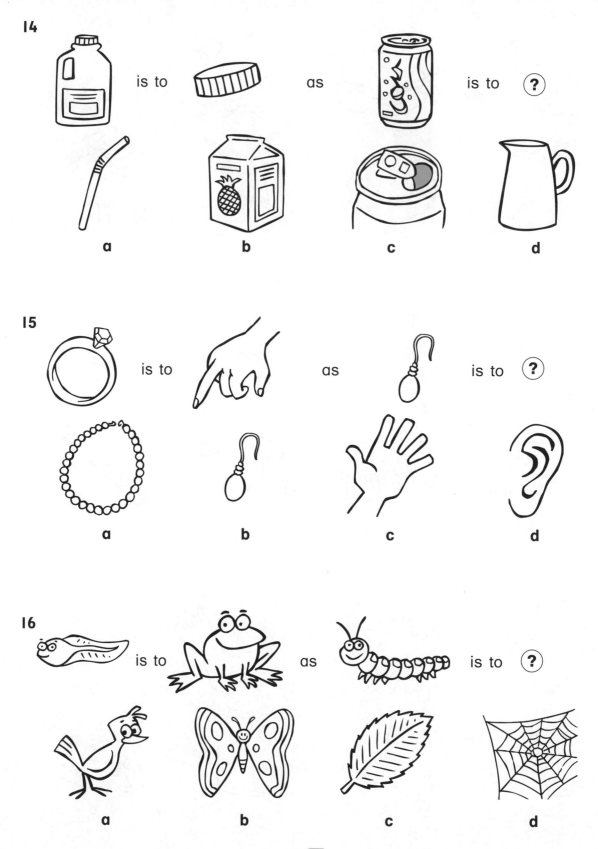

is to ... as ... is to ?

a   b   c   d

15

is to ... as ... is to ?

a   b   c   d

16

is to ... as ... is to ?

a   b   c   d

Which is the odd one out? Circle the letter.

Example

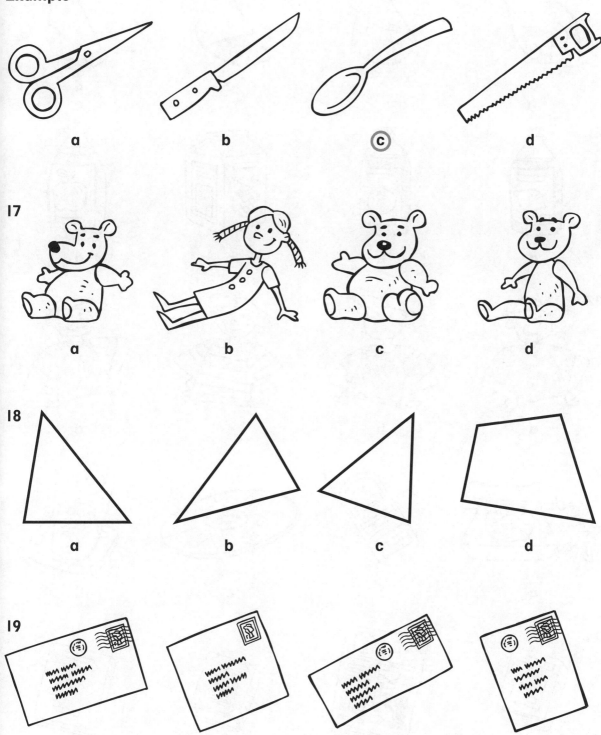

a   b   ⓒ   d

17

a   b   c   d

18

a   b   c   d

19

a   b   c   d

20

a b c d

21

a b c d

22

a b c d

23

a b c d

24

a b c d

Paper 3

Which picture completes the second pair in the same way as the first pair?
Circle the letter.

Example

3 is to ___ as ___ is to **?**

a   b   c   d

4 is to ___ as ___ is to **?**

a   b   c   d

5 is to ___ as ___ is to **?**

a   b   c   d

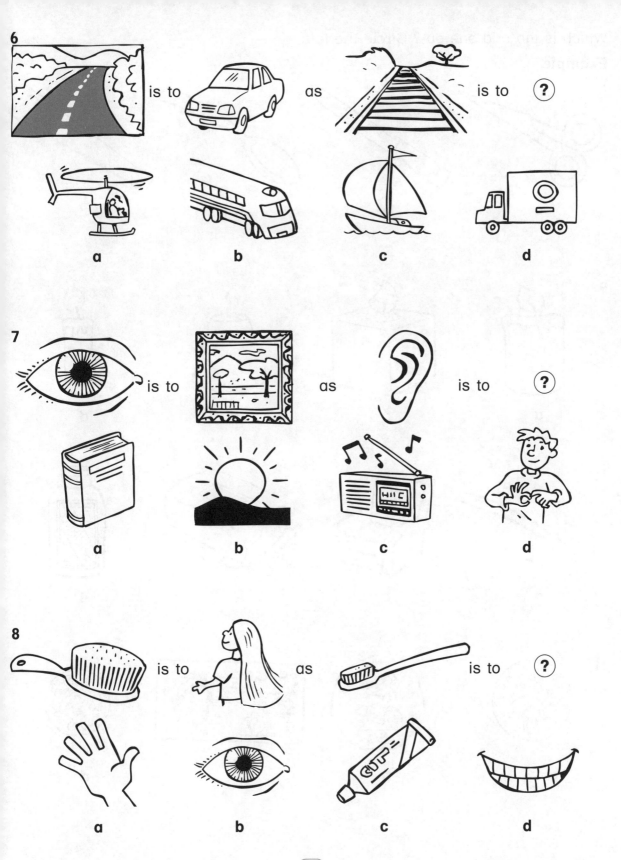

6 is to   as   is to   **?**

a   b   c   d

7 is to   as   is to   **?**

a   b   c   d

8 is to   as   is to   **?**

a   b   c   d

Which is the odd one out? Circle the letter.

Example

a   b   ⓒ   d

9

a   b   c   d

10

a   b   c   d

11

a   b   c   d

Paper 1

1	d
2	c
3	c
4	c
5	c
6	d
7	d
8	c
9	b
10	a
11	c
12	d
13	c
14	d
15	b
16	b
17	d
18	c
19	d
20	a
21	b
22	c
23	d
24	a

Paper 2

1	d
2	c
3	a
4	b
5	d
6	c
7	b
8	c
9	c
10	d
11	b
12	a
13	b
14	c
15	d
16	b
17	b
18	d
19	b
20	a
21	c
22	c
23	c
24	b

Paper 3

1 c
2 a
3 c
4 b
5 d
6 b
7 c
8 d
9 c
10 b
11 c
12 b
13 a
14 d
15 b
16 d
17 a
18 b
19 d
20 c
21 a
22 c
23 d
24 b

Paper 4

1 d
2 d
3 a
4 d
5 c
6 c
7 d
8 c
9 b
10 c
11 a
12 b
13 e
14 c
15 b
16 c
17 a
18 e
19 e
20 c
21 c
22 d
23 c
24 b

1	d
2	b
3	c
4	d
5	b
6	a
7	e
8	d
9	b
10	c
11	b
12	c
13	d
14	b
15	d
16	c
17	c
18	a
19	d
20	d
21	b
22	b
23	c
24	b

Bond Assessment Papers: Starter papers in Non-verbal Reasoning

ANSWERS

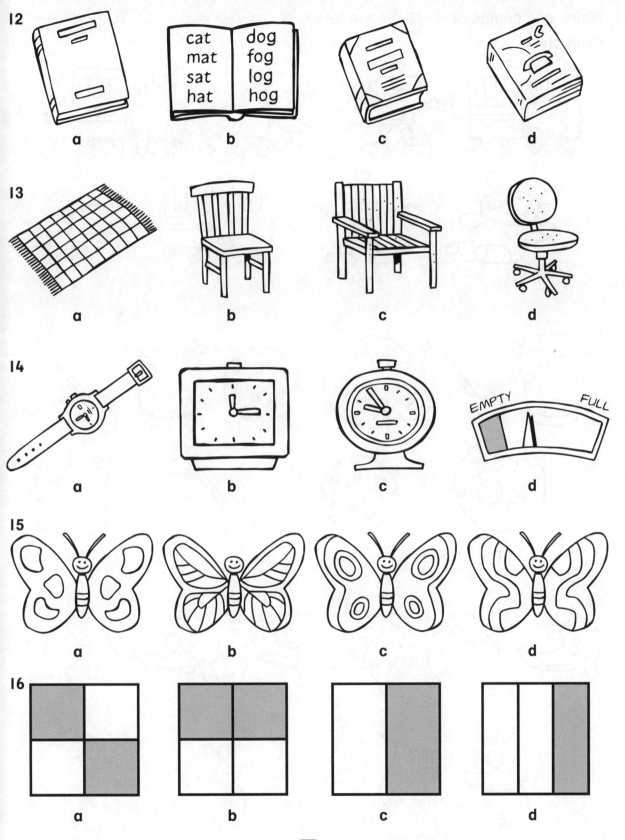

12   a   b   c   d

cat   dog
mat   fog
sat   log
hat   hog

13   a   b   c   d

14   a   b   c   d

EMPTY   FULL

15   a   b   c   d

16   a   b   c   d

Which one comes next? Circle the letter.

Example

a   b   c   d

17

a   b   c   d

18

a   b   c   d

24

19

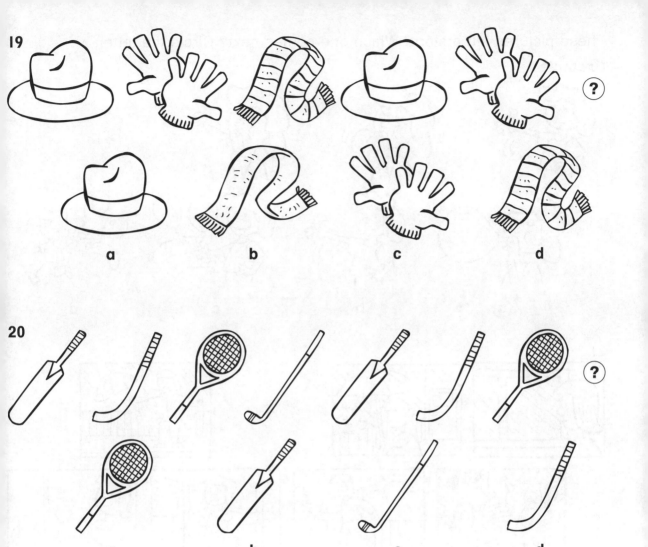

a   b   c   d

20

a   b   c   d

These pictures tell a story. Which one comes next? Circle the letter.

Example

a

b

c

d

21

a

b

c

d

22

a

b

c

d

23

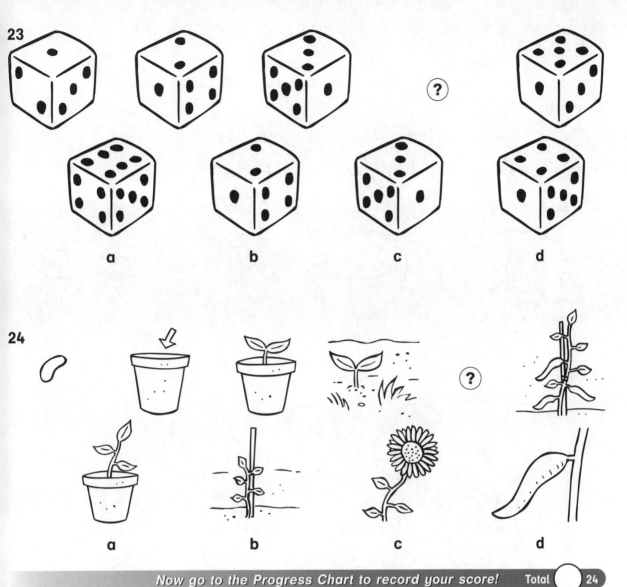

a   b   c   d

24

a   b   c   d

Now go to the Progress Chart to record your score!   Total   24

Paper 4

These pictures tell a story. Which one comes next? Circle the letter.

Example

3

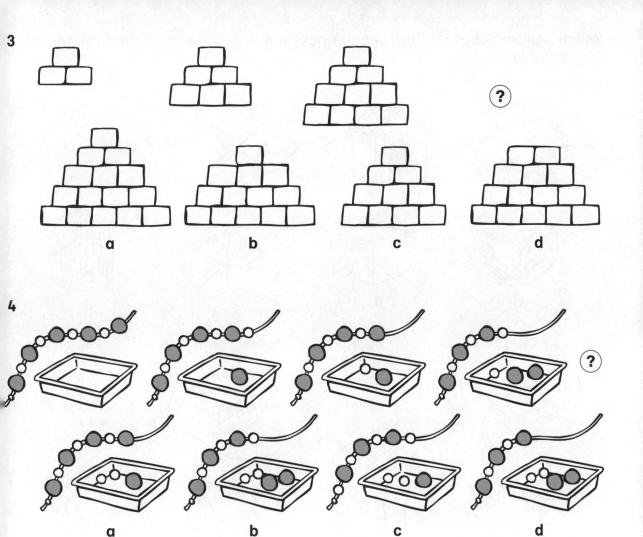

a   b   c   d

4

a   b   c   d

Which picture completes the second pair in the same way as the first pair? Circle the letter.

Example

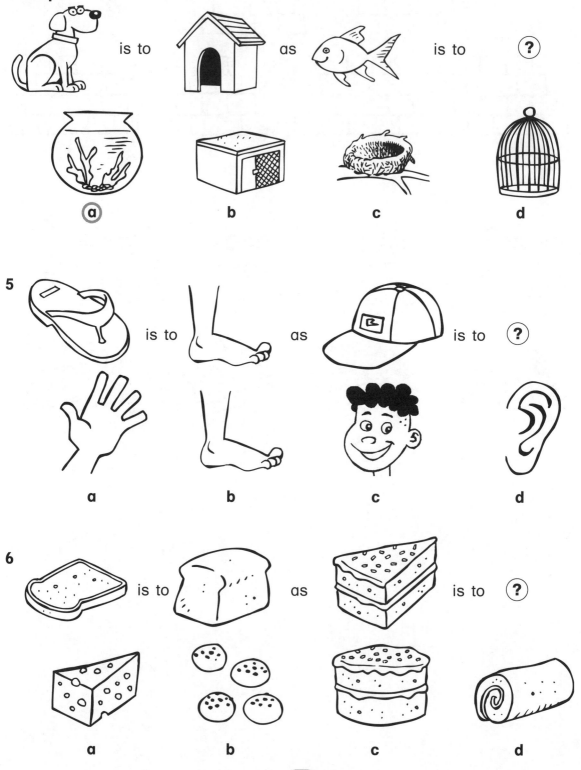

5

6

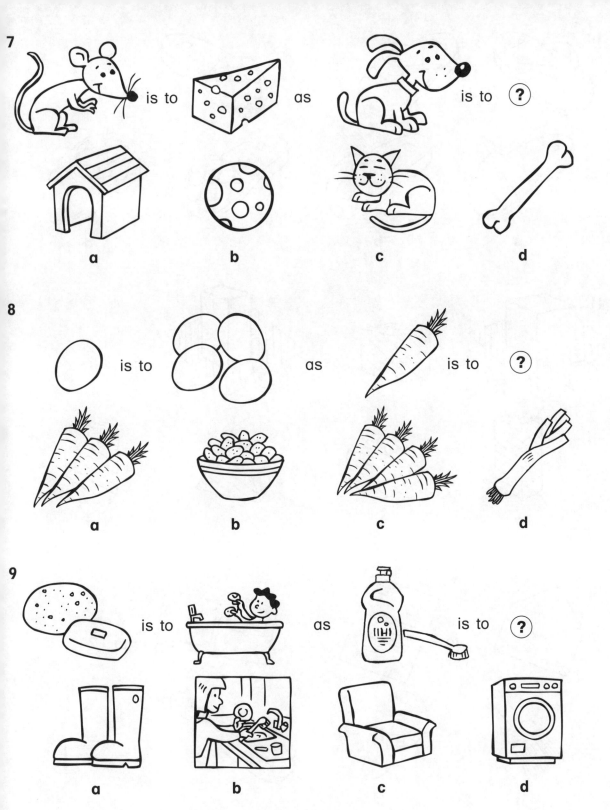

7

is to   as   is to   **?**

a   b   c   d

8

is to   as   is to   **?**

a   b   c   d

9

is to   as   is to   **?**

a   b   c   d

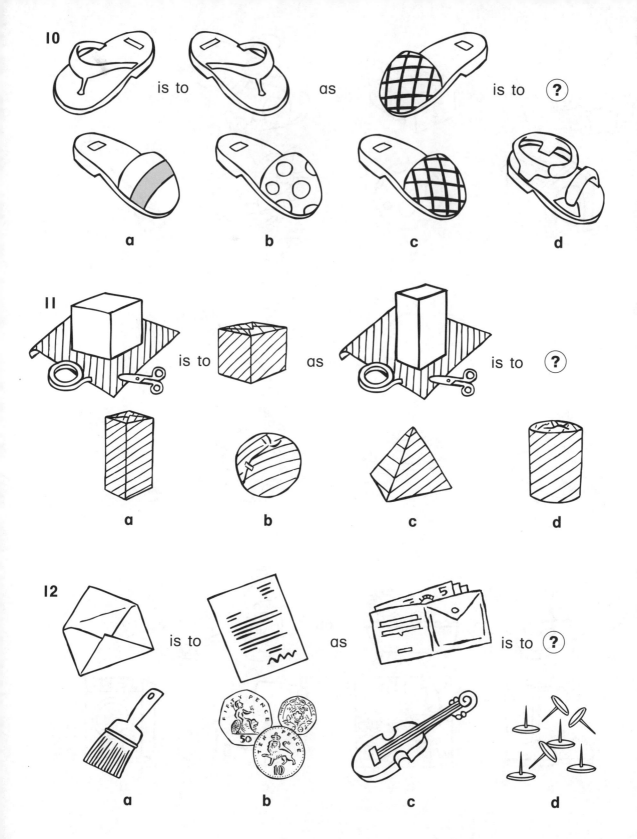

Which is the odd one out? Circle the letter.

Example

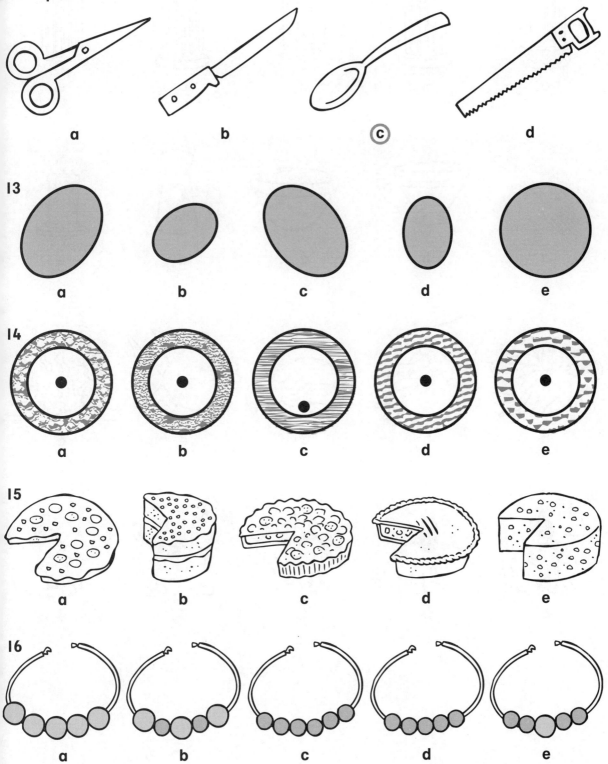

a   b   ©   d

13

a   b   c   d   e

14

a   b   c   d   e

15

a   b   c   d   e

16

a   b   c   d   e

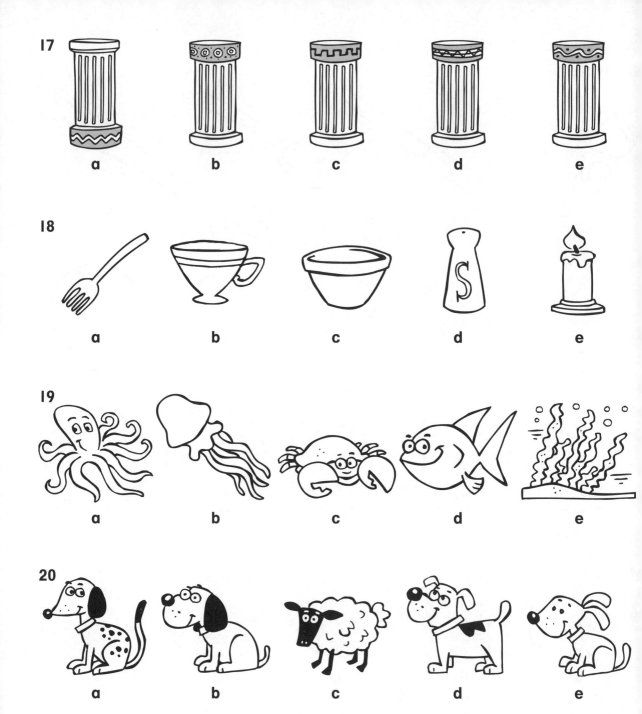

Which one comes next? Circle the letter.

Example

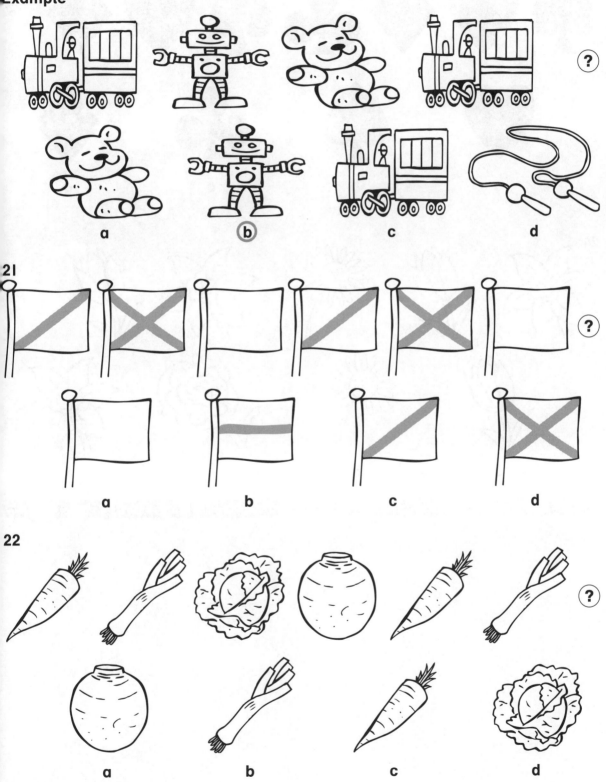

21

a   b   c   d

22

a   b   c   d

23

a   b   c   d

24

a   b   c   d

Now go to the Progress Chart to record your score!   Total   24

Paper 5

Which is the odd one out? Circle the letter.

Example

a   b   ⓒ   d

1
a   b   c   d   e

2
a   b   c   d   e

3
a   b   c   d   e

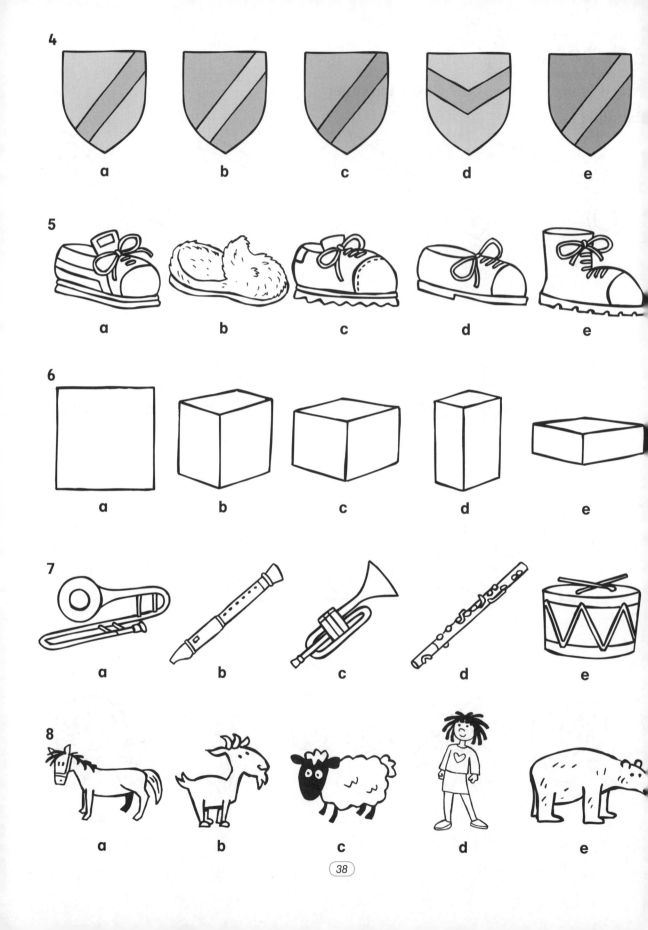

4
a   b   c   d   e

5
a   b   c   d   e

6
a   b   c   d   e

7
a   b   c   d   e

8
a   b   c   d   e

Which picture completes the second pair in the same way as the first pair?
Circle the letter.

Example

11 is to as is to ?

a b c d

12 is to as is to ?

a b c d

13 is to as is to ?

a b c d

14

is to   as   is to **(?)**

a   b   c   d

15

is to   as   is to **(?)**

a   b   c   d

16

is to   as   is to **(?)**

a   b   c   d

Which one comes next? Circle the letter.

Example

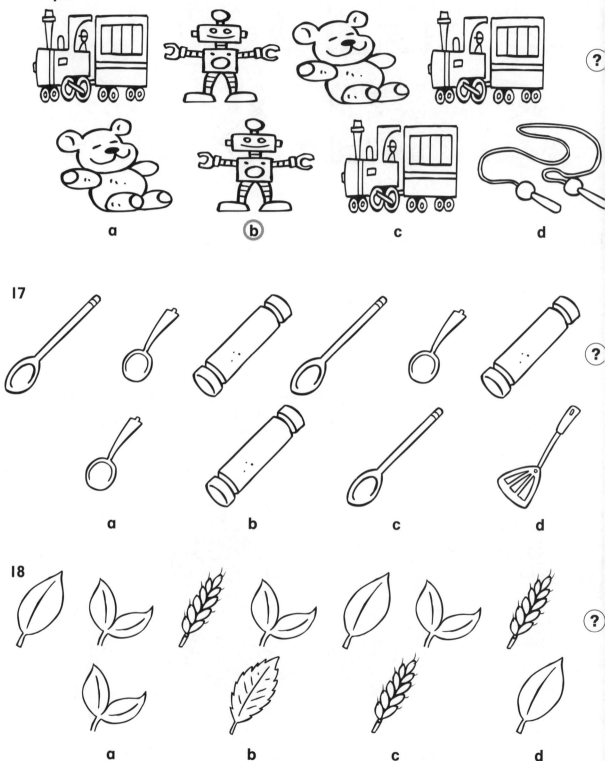

a

b

c

d

17

a

b

c

d

18

a

b

c

d

19

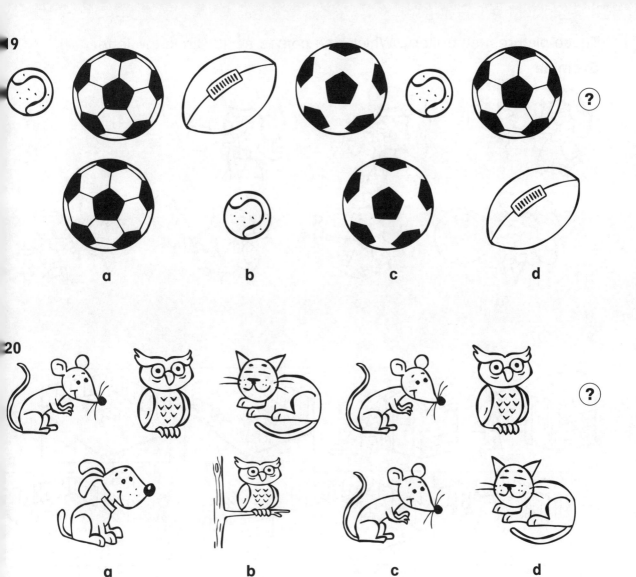

a b c d

20

a b c d

These pictures tell a story. Which one comes next? Circle the letter.

Example

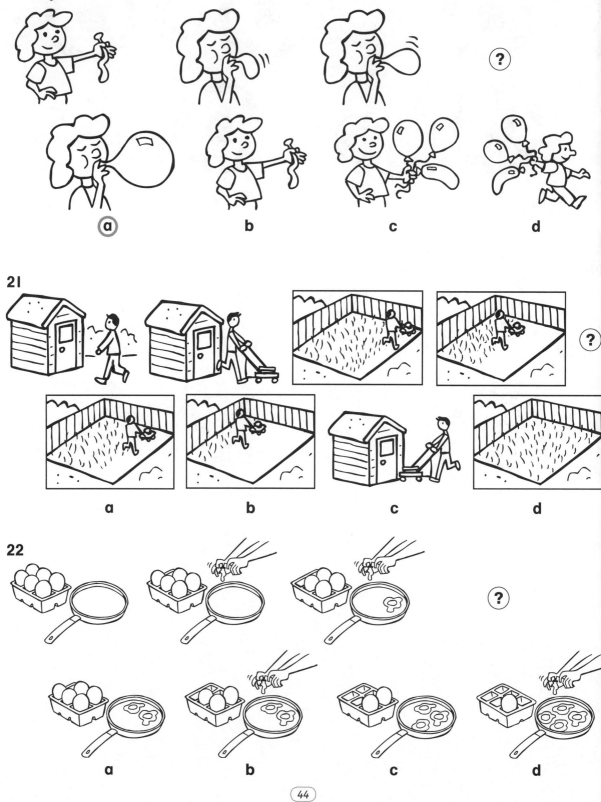

23

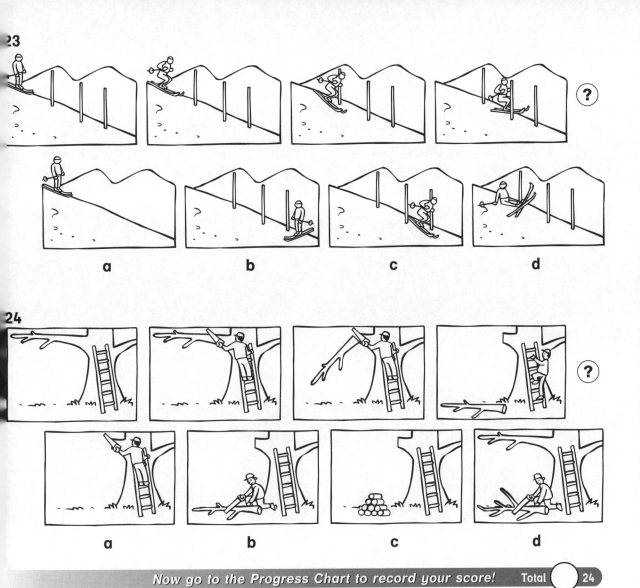

a

b

c

d

24

a

b

c

d

Now go to the Progress Chart to record your score! Total 24

45

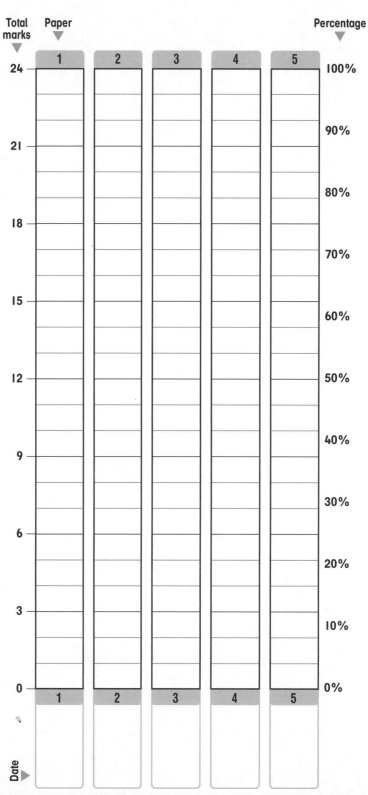